D1128377

KLINGER

A Story of Honor and Hope

written by

Betsy Beard

illustrated by

Shelley Johannes

Tragedy Assistance Program for Survivors
Washington, D.C.

Text and Illustrations Copyright ©2010
Tragedy Assistance Program for Survivors, Inc.
www.taps.org

and
T★A★P★S
are Registered U.S.Trademarks.
All rights reserved.

No part of this publication may be reproduced, stored in a retrieval system, or transmitted in any form or by any means, electronic, mechanical, photocopying, recording, or otherwise, without the prior written permission of the publisher.

ISBN Number 978-0-578-05431-5

Published by Tragedy Assistance Program for Survivors, Inc.
Written by Betsy Beard
Illustrations and book design by Shelley Johannes

CPSIA Compliance Information: Batch # 0310
For further information contact
RJ Communications, NY NY, 800-621-2556.

Manufactured in the United States of America

This book was written
In honor of
All of America's beloved fallen heroes

From the day he was born, Klinger's mother told him, "You are special."

His father said the same thing.

Even the boy who cleaned the stables told Klinger he was special.

Klinger dreamed of becoming the most special and famous race horse ever.

But...

He wasn't very good at running. Even the younger smaller horses were faster than Klinger. Still, he dreamed that someday he would be faster than the wind. After all, he was special... everyone said so.

On Klinger's third birthday, the trainer told Klinger's owner, "He's big and strong, but he's not very fast. I can't use him as a race horse. We will have to let him go."

Klinger hung his head. What would he do if he couldn't race? How would he ever be special?

The day arrived for Klinger to leave his home. He dragged himself up the ramp into the horse trailer. Everything would be different from now on.

He neighed goodbye to his father and mother. Who would think he was special now? As the truck started to move, a tear slid down Klinger's face.

The truck drove on and on...past the farms... over the mountains...through the cities. Finally the trailer stopped and the ramp was lowered.

Men, all dressed alike, came up the ramp to help Klinger. He lifted his head and sniffed the air. He smelled hay and oats and other horses. At least he would have new friends.

But where were the fields? All Klinger could see were buildings.

A man said, "Klinger, here's your new home," and led him into a stall with his name on the door.

"Where am I?" he asked the other horses.

STABLES

"You are in Fort Myer," a horse named Ranger said. "It's in Arlington, Virginia."

From the stall next to him Scout added, "Our trainers and riders are soldiers!"

"Is that why they all dress alike?" Klinger asked.

From another stall Babe answered, "Yes! And now you have been chosen to join the United States Army!"

Klinger had no idea what that meant. He hoped it would be something very special.

SCOUT
KLINGER

The next morning Klinger awakened to find his new friends groomed and outfitted in matching saddles and bridles. When they moved their heads, Klinger saw a shiny piece of metal on each halter.

He wondered what it was.

“We’re going to work!” Babe said.

Klinger knew their jobs must be very special to be dressed so splendidly. He wanted to wear a fancy outfit, too.

But first...

He had to be trained!

For weeks the soldiers worked with Klinger. They led him around and around in a circle. Then they put a heavy weight on his back. Finally Klinger was saddled and the soldiers rode him around the corral.

"Good job, Klinger!" the corporal said. "Now you are ready to learn more lessons."

Klinger pawed at the ground.

Every day Klinger worked hard to learn everything the soldiers taught him...

Like standing at attention until he was told to move... Like being brave when he heard loud noises... And not shying away when the flags flapped in the wind.

At long last the corporal told Klinger, "Now you are ready to take your place alongside the other horses."

Klinger would be part of the team! But why did he need all that training, just to get dressed up? That night Klinger asked the others.

Ranger held his head high and said, "We are the horses of the Caisson Platoon. We pull the wagons that take our nation's fallen heroes to their final resting places."

"There are no other horses like us in the whole world," Scout added.

"We bring comfort to the families by honoring their loved ones," said Babe. "It is a sad job, but we are proud to do it. If it were not for heroes who have given their lives, we would not live free."

"That does sound important," said Klinger.

Morning dawned.

"Today is your big day, Klinger!" said the corporal. "Let's get you ready."

Soldiers washed and groomed Klinger. They shined his hoofs. They trimmed his mane. As the corporal slipped a new halter over his nose and ears, Klinger saw a shiny piece of metal on it. It looked like the ones he saw on the other horses' halters that first day.

"This is your new halter, Klinger," said the corporal. "It holds your dog tag with your name engraved on it. From now on you will wear this dog tag, just like the rest of us soldiers."

Klinger stood at attention while the corporal and the sergeant hitched him and his friends to the empty Caisson wagon. Soldiers mounted and the sergeant gave the signal to start.

Klinger and the other Caisson horses obeyed the command. They pulled the wagon slowly into Arlington National Cemetery. They waited while soldiers lifted the casket onto the wagon and fastened the American flag around it.

Then the team started forward, following twenty-one paces behind the Chaplain. In front of the Chaplain, soldiers marched in formation. The band played music to honor the fallen hero.

As the family filed forward, Klinger could see their faces. Some were crying. A young boy clutched his sister's hand.

"Oh no!" Klinger thought, "The Soldier in the casket was their father..."

Klinger remembered how sad he was to leave his father and mother. A single tear made its way down his face. The children turned to stare at Klinger and he slowly nodded to them. He hoped they knew how much he cared.

Day after day...when it was cold...
when it was rainy...even if it snowed... Klinger worked, honoring each Soldier, Sailor, Marine, Airman, and Coastguardsman— men and women who had served and died.

Always he held his head high and looked right at the families. Klinger could sense their sadness. He was determined to honor their loved ones and show them he cared.

FORT · MYER

The days grew warm. The stables were abuzz with news.

"The most important day of the year is coming," said Ranger. "Memorial Day!"

"It's the day Americans honor those who have given their lives for freedom," Scout said.

"And we have extra special visitors coming to see us!" Babe told Klinger. "They are the children of our fallen heroes. Every year they come to TAPS Good Grief Camp to learn ways to help them deal with their sadness. That's why they come to see us!"

"But how can we help?" Klinger asked.

"You'll see!" Scout said.

KLINGE
ance Program for Sun

Just then the brother and sister whose father Klinger had honored on his first day raced toward him. He lowered his head so they could pet him. He nuzzled their hands and nibbled the treats they brought. He blew gently on their faces.

The children laughed and hugged him fiercely. Klinger whinnied. He knew he was more important than a race horse could ever be. His life was bringing honor to fallen heroes and comfort to their families.

Just as his mother and father had told him, he was special.

The Caisson Platoon

The Caisson Platoon is the last official full-time equestrian mounted unit in the Department of Defense. Its mission is to serve as the mounted escort for our nation's fallen heroes, providing Full Honor Military Funerals in Arlington National Cemetery. The platoon consists of 56 Soldiers who have volunteered from within The Old Guard. These hard-working Soldiers work weekends, holidays, and night shifts, since the horses need to be fed and cared for 24 hours a day. The Caisson Platoon is self-sufficient, staffed with a Farrier, a Saddler, a Horse Trainer, a Vet Tech, and a Veterinarian. Caisson Soldiers take complete care of the horses on a daily basis.

The 53 Caisson Horses are either black or white. They are workhorses such as Morgans, Percherons, Quarter horses, or a cross-breed. Seven matching horses serve on each Caisson Team: two Wheel Horses, two Swing Horses, two Lead Horses, and one Section Horse. The horses get a haircut each week. Every six weeks they are re-shod. The Field Artillery harnesses in use date from before 1915 and the saddles are modified McClellan Saddles, designed by General McClellan in 1859 to ease the pressure on the horse's spine.

Historically, Caisson Wagons were first used in the early 1800's. Caisson refers to the ammunition boxes were on the wagon. The wagons took ammunition, spare parts, rations, and supplies to the front, bringing wounded and dead soldiers back on the return trip. The Caisson Wagons brought hope to the wounded and dignity to the final journey of the dead. The 2,500 pound Caisson Wagons currently in use date from 1918 and have been refitted to carry flag-draped caskets.

Good Grief Camp

TAPS is the leading organization providing emotional support to the children of Armed Forces members who have died while serving our country, regardless of the circumstances of the death. The only program of its kind in the nation, TAPS hosts Regional Good Grief Camps throughout the year as well as the National Military Survivor Seminar and Good Grief Camp for young survivors in our nation's capital during Memorial Day weekend.

TAPS gathers some of the nation's best grief and trauma experts to help the children share, heal, honor their loved ones, and have some fun in a safe, caring environment. At the National Good Grief Camp, TAPS also trains members of the military as mentors to partner one-on-one with a grieving child. The mentor helps the child learn to cope with feelings of loss, and understand that the military still supports them and that they will always be a part of the military family. In addition to grief work, young survivors meet and forge lasting friendships with other children who have experienced a loss. This reinforces the understanding that they are not alone in their journey of grief.

Surrounded by the memorials in Washington, D.C., children learn about our nation's capital and the legacy of Americans who have served and sacrificed in defense of our way of life. They learn that their loved one is a part of that legacy and gain a sense of how our nation honors those who serve.

T★A★P★S

The Tragedy Assistance Program for Survivors (TAPS) is America's support group for all whose lives have been forever changed by the death of a loved one serving in the Armed Forces. TAPS provides immediate and long-term emotional help, hope, and healing to anyone grieving the death of a loved one in military service to America, regardless of their relationship to the deceased or the circumstances of the death.

Tragedy Assistance Program for Survivors (TAPS) is a national nonprofit Veterans Service Organization offering peer-based emotional support, grief and trauma resources, casework assistance, and crisis intervention care at no cost to the surviving families.

For more information about TAPS,
visit our website at www.taps.org.

T★A★P★S

★SUPPORTS★

the bereaved survivor through a network of Peer Mentors. Mentors are volunteers who have also lost a loved one in the Armed Forces and are now standing by to reach out and support others.

★PROVIDES★

a national toll-free help and information line 24 hours a day, seven days a week at 800-959-TAPS (8277). Support is available from leading experts in the field of grief and trauma.

★PUBLISHES★

a quarterly magazine focusing on vital issues facing military survivors. The magazine is sent free of charge to survivors, commanders, chaplains, casualty staff, and caregivers.

★HOSTS★

the TAPS Online Community of survivors, providing secure chat rooms, message boards, peer group discussion sites, and an extensive website at www.taps.org.

★SPONSORS★

Military Survivor Seminars for adults and Good Grief Camps for young survivors in locations across America. These seminars give survivors the opportunity to learn, grow, share, and help each other heal.

★CONNECTS★

survivors to community-based resources and provides grief and trauma resources and information.

About Klinger

Klinger is a black Percheron Morgan Cross Breed with a white star on his forehead. He stands more than 16 hands high and weighs 1400 pounds. Klinger was born in Lamar, Iowa and worked as a farm horse until he was three years old. He was donated to the Caisson Platoon on March 1, 2003. Klinger is so gentle and easy-going that he will allow the soldiers to sit on him when he is lying down.

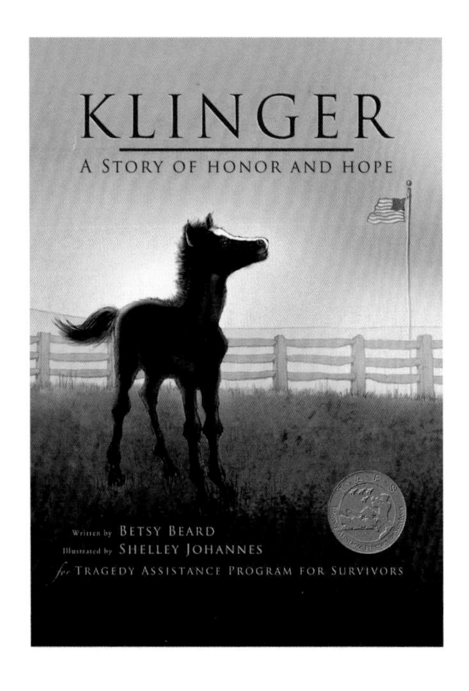

About the Book

Years ago the children and mentors of the TAPS Good Grief Camp began the tradition of visiting the stables at Fort Myer during the TAPS National Military Survivor Seminar. They fell in love with Klinger, one of the largest and gentlest Caisson horses stationed there. Because of the comfort the children received from Klinger, TAPS Founder Bonnie Carroll conceived the idea of a children's book that would showcase Klinger's connection to the courageous children of TAPS.

About the Author

Betsy Beard is the editor of TAPS Magazine, a quarterly publication of Tragedy Assistance Program for Survivors. She lives in North Carolina with her husband, Randy, near their daughter, Staci. Their lives were forever changed by the death of their only son and brother, Army Specialist Bradley S. Beard, who was killed in support of Operation Iraqi Freedom in 2004. In the years since Brad's death, the family has found help, hope, and healing within TAPS.

About the Illustrator

Shelley Johannes began her career as an architectural designer with a BS in Architecture. After the birth of her first child, her newfound passion for motherhood unexpectedly led her career into the world of children's book illustration. Four years and ten books later, Shelley has the best of both worlds. She plays all day and draws late into the night. She lives in Michigan with her husband Bob and their two boys, Matthew and Nolan.

THANK YOU

These materials were made possible by a grant from the American Legion Child Welfare Foundation, Inc. TAPS extends its sincere gratitude to the American Legion Child Welfare Foundation for its invaluable financial support in helping this book to become a reality.

American Legion Child Welfare Foundation

We are also grateful for the cooperation of the United States Army Caisson Platoon of Fort Myer. We thank those who serve for sharing their world and the solemn duties they perform with compassion and purpose.

We acknowledge the heartfelt support of the TAPS family: staff members, supporters, volunteers, and friends, who make possible our mission of care and comfort.

We salute the precious children and teens of the TAPS Good Grief Camp. They are the living legacy of the brave men and women of our Armed Forces, and their courage continues to inspire us.